# Higher

# Art & Design

## 2000 Exam
Paper 1 Practical Assignment
Paper 2

## 2001 Exam
Paper 1 Practical Assignment
Paper 2

## 2002 Exam
Paper 1 Practical Assignment
Paper 2

## 2003 Exam
Paper 1 Practical Assignment
Paper 2

© Scottish Qualifications Authority

All rights reserved. Copying prohibited. No part of this publication may be reproduced, stored in a retrieval system, or transmitted in any form or by any means, electronic, mechanical, photo-copying, recording or otherwise.

First exam published in 2000.
Published by
Leckie & Leckie, 8 Whitehill Terrace, St. Andrews, Scotland KY16 8RN
tel: 01334 475656  fax: 01334 477392
enquiries@leckieandleckie.co.uk www.leckieandleckie.co.uk

Leckie & Leckie Project Team: Peter Dennis; John MacPherson; Bruce Ryan; Andrea Smith

ISBN 1-84372-133-3

A CIP Catalogue record for this book is available from the British Library.

Printed in Scotland by Scotprint.

Leckie & Leckie is a division of Granada Learning Limited, part of Granada plc.

Leckie×Leckie
Scotland's leading educational publishers

# Introduction

Dear Student,

This past paper book provides you with the perfect opportunity to put into practice everything you should know in order to excel in your exams. The compilation of papers will expose you to an extensive range of questions and will provide you with a clear idea of what to expect in your own exam this summer.

The past papers represent an integral part of your revision: the questions test not only your subject knowledge and understanding but also the examinable skills that you should have acquired and developed throughout your course. The answer booklet at the back of the book will allow you to monitor your ability, see exactly what an examiner looks for to award full marks and will also enable you to identify areas for more concentrated revision. Make use too of the frequent tips for revision and sitting your exam to ensure you perform to the best of your ability on the day.

Practice makes perfect. This book should prove an invaluable revision aid and will help you prepare to succeed.

Good luck!

# Acknowledgements

Leckie & Leckie is grateful to the copyright holders, as credited on page 84. Every effort has been made to trace the copyright holders and to obtain their permission for the use of copyright material. Leckie & Leckie will gladly receive information enabling them to rectify any error or omission in subsequent editions.

# 2000 HIGHER

# X003/301

NATIONAL
QUALIFICATIONS
2000

ART AND DESIGN
HIGHER
Paper 1
Practical Assignment

**The Practical Examinations for the 2000 examination diet may take place at the centre's discretion on the most convenient date in the period from Tuesday 2 May until Friday 12 May inclusive.**

**Time allowed: 3 hours**

50 marks are assigned to this paper.

Maximum sizes:    Two-dimensional work: A2.
                    Three-dimensional work: 30 cm in greatest dimension.

Any medium except oil paint may be used.

SCOTTISH
QUALIFICATIONS
AUTHORITY
©

## GENERAL INSTRUCTIONS

Base your work for the Practical Assignment on your Expressive Activity unit **or** your Design Activity unit.

In the examination room you may refer to:

- Design **or** Expressive Folio of work
- Practical Assignment Form/Course Review Statement

You may use any three-dimensional source materials identified in the unit you have selected.

You will be allowed up to 20 minutes after the examination to assemble your work on the maximum number of sheets (2 × A2 sheets).

**This extension time is not to be used for producing examination work.**

Select **either** SECTION A **or** SECTION B.

## SECTION A

### Expressive Activity

### Task

You should produce practical work which demonstrates an alternative approach or approaches to work carried out in your Expressive unit. This could take the form of new and further developments from your stimulus and might include extending ideas not fully explored within the work of your unit.

**Remember that work produced for this Assignment should relate to your overall EXPRESSIVE unit theme and must not simply be a copy of work already undertaken.**

It is important that you develop your **own** ideas. The following suggestions are provided to help you get started:

- produce work based on the stimulus or sources used by you but not fully explored for your Expressive folio
- produce work which emphasises different use of visual elements from those explored in your unit
- explore a different interpretation or style of approach to your chosen theme.

Work should be on a maximum of **two** A2 sheets or equivalent three-dimensional work. You may use any appropriate media, materials or process.

## SECTION B

### Design Activity

### Task

You should produce practical work which demonstrates an alternative approach or approaches to work carried out in your Design unit. This could take the form of new and further developments from your brief and might include extending Design issue(s) not fully explored within the work of your unit.

**Remember that work produced for this Assignment should relate to your DESIGN brief and design issue(s) and must not simply be a copy of work already undertaken.**

It is important that you develop your **own** ideas. The following suggestions are provided to help you get started:

- develop work based on a design issue which you considered but did not fully explore in your Design unit
- develop design ideas which extend the issues and solution in your unit
- your client asks you to reconsider your solution and suggest further modifications and/or changes which may be considered improvements.

Work should be on a maximum of **two** A2 sheets or equivalent three-dimensional work. You may use any appropriate media, materials or process.

*[END OF QUESTION PAPER]*

**Blank page**

# X003/302

NATIONAL
QUALIFICATIONS
2000

WEDNESDAY, 24 MAY
1.00 PM – 3.00 PM

ART AND DESIGN
HIGHER
Paper 2

There are **two** sections to this paper, Section 1— Art Studies; and Section 2— Design Studies. Each section is worth 40 marks.

Candidates should attempt questions as follows:

In SECTION 1 answer **ONE full question** (parts (a) and (b)), and **ONE part (a) only** of any other question

**and**

In SECTION 2 answer **ONE full question** (parts (a) and (b)), and **ONE part (a) only** of any other question.

**Reference materials** are supplied in a separate paper inserted inside the front cover of this paper. Check that you have the Reference Sheets before the examination begins.

SCOTTISH
QUALIFICATIONS
AUTHORITY
©

# SECTION 1—ART STUDIES

Answer **ONE full question**, (parts (a) and (b)), and **ONE part (a)** *only* of any other question.

(i)

Peter Howson "The Heroic Dosser" (1987) oil on canvas (213.5 x 213.5cm)

*Marks*

1. **Portraiture**

   (*a*) Illustration (i) is a portrait by Peter Howson. Evaluate the painting in detail. Comment on the artist's use of colour and tone. How successful do you think the artist has been in making his subject appear powerful? **10**

   (*b*) Select **two** artists you have studied. Explain why you consider their work in portraiture to be historically important. Refer to specific examples. **20**

# SECTION 1—ART STUDIES (continued)

(ii)

Edgar Degas "The Rehearsal" (1873-4) pastel on canvas (59 x 83.3cm)

*Marks*

## 2. Figure Composition

(a) Illustration (ii) shows "The Rehearsal" by Edgar Degas. Analyse the painting in detail. Comment on the artist's use of colour and treatment of light. Discuss the methods used by Degas to convey a sense of frozen movement.

**10**

(b) Discuss in detail the work of **two** artists from different periods whose figure compositions have impressed you. Describe the methods used by the artists to communicate their ideas or feelings.

**20**

# SECTION 1—ART STUDIES (continued)

(iii)

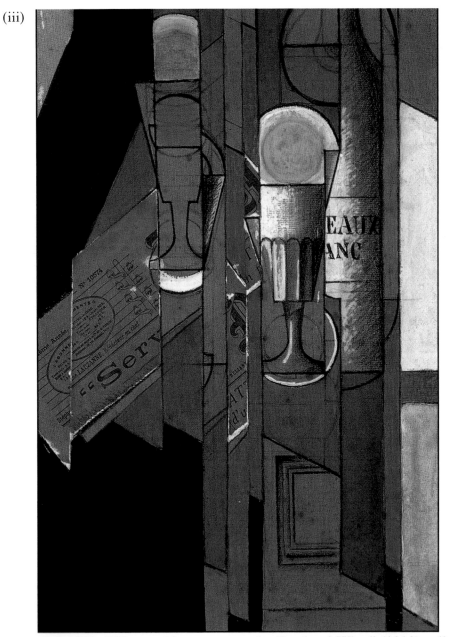

Juan Gris "Glasses, Newspaper and a Bottle of Wine" (1913) collage, gouache watercolour, coloured chalks on paper (45 x 29cm)

*Marks*

3. **Still Life**

   (a) Illustration (iii) is a still life by Juan Gris. Discuss the painting and comment on the use of the following: shape, colour, choice of media. What is your opinion of this fragmented composition?　　**10**

   (b) Analyse in detail **two** examples of still life painting by artists working in different styles. Explain to what extent you consider the examples to be successful and in what ways they are typical of the artists' styles.　　**20**

## SECTION 1—ART STUDIES (continued)

(iv)

Andy Goldsworthy "Sidewinder" (1985) wood construction (2 x 100 metres approx.)

*Marks*

**4. Natural Environment**

    (*a*)    Illustration (iv) is a sculpture by Andy Goldsworthy. It is made from trees bent by the wind. Analyse the sculpture and comment on scale, choice of materials and the title of the piece. This sculpture is a response to the natural environment in which it was made. What are your personal responses to the sculpture?    **10**

    (*b*)    Select **two** artists you have studied. Discuss examples of their work. Explain in what ways their work is a response to the natural environment.    **20**

# SECTION 1—ART STUDIES (continued)

(v)

Fernand Léger "The Constructors" (1950) oil on canvas (299.8 x 200cm)

*Marks*

5.  **Built Environment**

   (a)  Illustration (v) is a painting by Fernand Léger. Evaluate this response by Léger to a built environment and those at work in it. Comment on colour, shape and composition. Discuss the methods used by Léger to convey a sense of space.   **10**

   (b)  Analyse in detail the work of at least **two** artists who have used the built environment for inspiration. Explain what aspects of their work you have found particularly interesting and impressive.   **20**

# SECTION 1—ART STUDIES (continued)

(vi)

Salvador Dali "Autumnal Cannibalism" (1936) oil on canvas (65 x 62.5cm)

*Marks*

6. **Fantasy and Imagination**

   (a) Illustration (vi) is a painting by Salvador Dali. Discuss the work in detail. Dali described his paintings as "Dream Photographs". What aspects of this example do you think contribute to this view? How important is the title to your understanding of the painting?

   **10**

   (b) Analyse and discuss **two** examples of work, by important artists, based on fantasy and imagination. Explain the methods used by the artists to communicate their ideas.

   **20**

# SECTION 2—DESIGN STUDIES

Answer **ONE full question**, (parts (a) and (b)), and **ONE part (a)** *only* of any other question.

(vii)

War poster (1940)

Marks

7.    **Graphic Design**

    (*a*) Illustration (vii) shows a Second World War poster. Comment on the methods used in the design to convey information. How does the photography contribute to the overall impact of the poster? What is your opinion of the poster?　　**10**

    (*b*) The twentieth century has seen immense changes in graphic design. Discuss these changes making reference to specific examples.　　**20**

## SECTION 2—DESIGN STUDIES (continued)

(viii)

Philippe Starck "Juicy Salif" 1989
cast aluminium lemon squeezer

*Marks*

### 8. Product Design

(a) Illustration (viii) shows Philippe Starck's lemon squeezer. Evaluate the success of this object in terms of form and function. Compare Starck's design with the form and function of other kitchen utensils you have used at home.

**10**

(b) Starck's design probably has its sources in nature. Discuss other product designers or design movements which have used natural sources for inspiration.

**20**

## SECTION 2—DESIGN STUDIES (continued)

(ix)

Gerrit Rietveld, Schroder House interior (1924)

*Marks*

### 9. Interior Design

(a) Illustration (ix) shows the interior of the Schroder House designed by Gerrit Rietveld in 1924. Comment on the way in which Rietveld uses colour, line and shape in order to create this style of interior.

**10**

(b) Rietveld's interiors have strong sense of unity. Discuss the interior(s) of any other designer, or group of designers, displaying a similar sense of unity.

**20**

# SECTION 2—DESIGN STUDIES (continued)

(x)

Alexander "Greek" Thomson, St Vincent Street Church, Glasgow, (1857-1859), sandstone

*Marks*

## 10. Environmental/Architectural Design

(a) Illustration (x) shows Alexander "Greek" Thomson's design for a church in Glasgow. Discuss the architectural style of this building and comment on the architect's use of the sloping site to create a powerful effect. Why do you think this church has sometimes been called a temple?    **10**

(b) Discuss the relationship between form and function in the work of any architects or environmental designers you have studied.    **20**

## SECTION 2—DESIGN STUDIES (continued)

(xi)

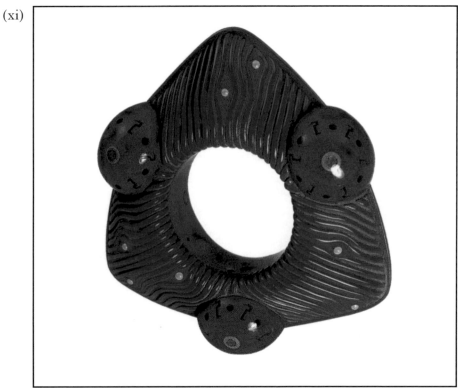

Peter Chang, Bracelet (1988) acrylic, PVC, found objects

*Marks*

## 11. Jewellery Design

(a) Illustration (xi) shows a bracelet designed and made by Peter Chang. What do you think of Chang's use of materials and treatment of form in this design? Give specific reasons for your views.

**10**

(b) Discuss the working methods of any jewellery designer you have studied. Make reference to their visual sources and use of materials.

**20**

## SECTION 2—DESIGN STUDIES (continued)

(xii)

Zandra Rhodes, "Conceptual chic" (1977) Punk jersey dresses

## 12. Textile Design

*Marks*

(a) Illustration (xii) shows Zandra Rhodes' Punk jersey dresses designed in 1977. Comment on the methods she has used in order to explore the potential of this fabric. How effective is her introduction of street-style elements into fashion designs?

**10**

(b) With reference to the work of **one or more** fashion or textile designers you have studied discuss how they have used materials in new and creative ways.

**20**

**Blank page**

2001 HIGHER

# X003/301

NATIONAL
QUALIFICATIONS
2001

# ART AND DESIGN
## HIGHER
Paper 1
Practical Assignment

**The Practical Examinations for the 2001 examination diet may take place at the centre's discretion on the most convenient date in the period from Monday 30 April until Friday 11 May inclusive.**

**Time allowed: 3 hours**

50 marks are assigned to this paper.

Maximum sizes:    Two-dimensional work: A2.
Three-dimensional work: 30 cm in greatest dimension.

Any medium except oil paint may be used.

SCOTTISH
QUALIFICATIONS
AUTHORITY
©

## GENERAL INSTRUCTIONS

Base your work for the Practical Assignment on your Expressive Activity unit **or** your Design Activity unit.

In the examination room you may refer to:

• Design **or** Expressive Folio of work

• Practical Assignment Form/Course Review Statement

You may use any three-dimensional source materials identified in the unit you have selected.

You will be allowed up to 20 minutes after the examination to assemble your work on the maximum number of sheets (2 × A2 sheets).

**This extension time is not to be used for producing examination work.**

Note: Mechanical reproductions of drawings and/or photographs from your folio by means such as TRACING, LIGHT BOXES and PHOTOCOPYING **will not be permitted during the examination.**

Select **either** SECTION A **or** SECTION B.

## SECTION A

### Expressive Activity

### Task

You should produce practical work which demonstrates your ability to develop and/or refine work carried out in your Expressive unit. This could take the form of new and further developments from your stimulus and might include extending ideas not fully explored within the work of your unit leading to alternative outcome(s).

**Remember that work produced for this Assignment should relate directly to your EXPRESSIVE unit theme and must develop, not simply copy, work already done. Further investigative work, such as analytical drawing, is not appropriate in this assignment.**

The following suggestions are provided to help you get started:

• produce work based on the stimulus or sources used by you but not fully explored in your Expressive unit

• produce work which emphasises a different style of approach to your chosen theme.

Work should be on a maximum of **two** A2 sheets or equivalent three-dimensional work. You may use any suitable media, materials or process.

**SECTION B**

**Design Activity**

**Task**

You should produce practical work which demonstrates an alternative approach or approaches to work carried out in your Design unit. This could take the form of new and further developments from your brief and might include extending Design ideas not fully explored within the work of your unit.

**Remember that work produced for this Assignment should relate to your DESIGN brief and design unit and must develop, not simply copy, work already done. Further investigative work, such as analytical drawing, is not appropriate in this assignment.**

The following suggestions are provided to help you get started:

- develop design ideas which you considered but did not fully explore in your Design unit

- reconsider your solution and suggest further modifications and/or changes to improve it.

Work should be on a maximum of **two** A2 sheets or equivalent three-dimensional work. You may use any suitable media, materials or process.

*[END OF QUESTION PAPER]*

**Blank page**

# X003/302

NATIONAL
QUALIFICATIONS
2001

FRIDAY, 18 MAY
1.30PM – 3.30PM

ART AND DESIGN
HIGHER
Paper 2

There are **two** sections to this paper, Section 1—Art Studies; and Section 2—Design Studies. Each section is worth 40 marks.

Candidates should attempt questions as follows:

In SECTION 1 answer **ONE full question** (parts (*a*) and (*b*)) and **ONE part (*a*) only** of any other question

**and**

In SECTION 2 answer **ONE full question** (parts (*a*) and (*b*)) and **ONE part (*a*) only** of any other question.

SCOTTISH
QUALIFICATIONS
AUTHORITY
©

## SECTION 1—ART STUDIES

### Instructions

Answer **ONE full question**, (parts (*a*) and (*b*)), and **ONE part (*a*) only** of any other question.

Elisabeth Frink "Goggle Head" (1969) bronze (62·2 cm)

*Marks*

## 1. Portraiture

(*a*) The illustration is of a sculpture by Elisabeth Frink. Discuss the use of texture and form. Comment on the artist's choice of subject and her treatment of it. What is your personal reaction to this sculpted portrait? **10**

(*b*) Discuss the work of **two** artists from different periods whose work in portraiture has impressed you. Explain why you consider them to be important artists. **20**

## SECTION 1—ART STUDIES (continued)

George Grosz "Berlin Streetscene" (1930) watercolour, ink and oil on paper (60 × 46cm)

*Marks*

## 2. Figure Composition

Grosz lived in Germany during a period of economic depression. He used political satire and caricature to express his views about society.

(*a*) It has been said "Grosz is a master at showing social and political comment through his work". Discuss this statement in terms of the subject matter, inter-relationships of figures and the artist's use of line and colour.          **10**

(*b*) Select **two** artists from different periods. Discuss examples of their figure compositions. Comment on the methods used by the artists to communicate their ideas. Explain why you consider them to be successful artists.          **20**

**[Turn over**

**SECTION 1—ART STUDIES (continued)**

W. Y. MacGregor "The Vegetable Stall" (1884) oil on canvas (105 × 150cm)

*Marks*

## 3. Still Life

(a) The illustration is of a painting by W. Y. MacGregor.
Discuss the composition of the painting. Comment on the artist's use of colour and handling of the various textures in the still life group. What is your opinion of this painting? **10**

(b) Compare examples of work in still life by **two** artists from different periods. Discuss the similarities and differences in their choice of subject matter, working methods and style. **20**

**SECTION 1—ART STUDIES (continued)**

Duncan Shanks "Fruit Fields" (1990) acrylic on paper with collage (41cm × 44cm)

## 4. Natural Environment

*Marks*

(*a*)  The illustration is of a painting by Duncan Shanks.  Comment on the use of visual elements and handling of media.  Discuss the artist's personal response to this rural subject.  What is your opinion of this painting?  **10**

(*b*)  The natural environment, as a theme, has always inspired artists.  Compare and contrast the works of **two** artists from different periods.  Your comparison should discuss the different approaches and responses of the artists to the theme.  **20**

**[Turn over**

## SECTION 1—ART STUDIES (continued)

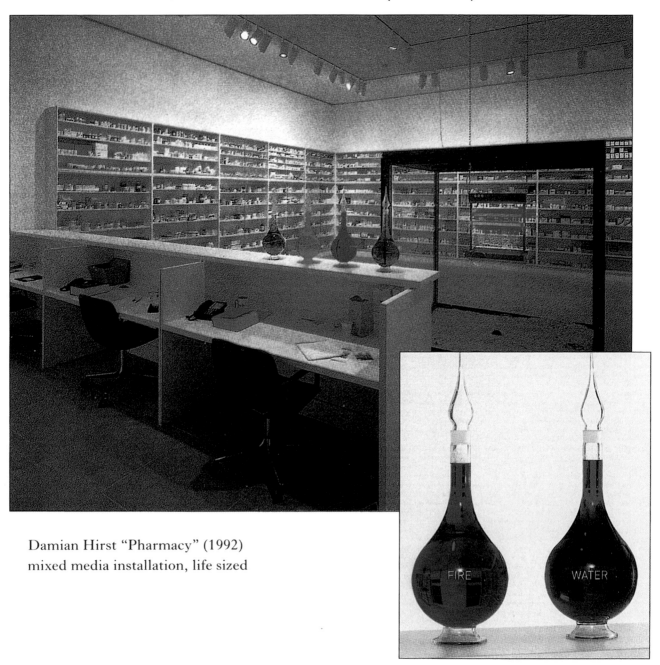

Damian Hirst "Pharmacy" (1992)
mixed media installation, life sized

(detail)

*Marks*

## 5. Built Environment

Hirst has used the full range of shop fittings and medicines dispensed in a chemist's shop as the medium for this installation set up in a gallery. The viewer can enter the actual space. Hirst says, "All pharmaceutical drugs exist in the space between birth and death. The drugs are meant to keep you alive."

(*a*) What do you think Hirst is trying to tell us about life today? Give your opinion of his use of real-life objects as a medium for art. **10**

(*b*) Discuss examples of work by **two** artists from different periods who have been inspired by the built environment. Explain how your chosen examples are typical of your artists' styles and why you consider them to be important artists. **20**

**SECTION 1—ART STUDIES (continued)**

Henri Rousseau "The Sleeping Gypsy" (1897) oil on canvas (123cm × 197cm)

*Marks*

## 6. Fantasy and Imagination

(a) The illustration is of a painting by Henri Rousseau. Comment on the artist's use of colour and light. Discuss the methods used to create this dream like work. What is your personal interpretation of the painting? **10**

(b) Select **two** artists from different periods. Compare and contrast examples of their work. Discuss the methods used by the artists to communicate their ideas on the theme of fantasy and imagination. Comment on your personal responses to their work. **20**

**[Turn over**

## SECTION 2—DESIGN STUDIES

**Instructions**

Answer **ONE full question**, (parts (*a*) and (*b*)), and **ONE part (*a*) only** of any other question.

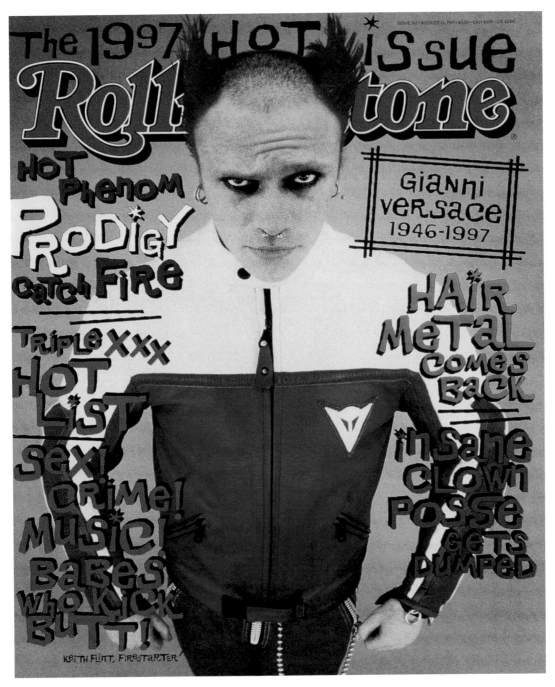

Front cover of Rolling Stone Magazine (August 1997)

*Marks*

## 7. Graphic Design

(*a*) Explore, in detail, the way in which the designer uses colour, lettering and photography in order to create a particularly striking magazine cover. What other factors contribute to the effectiveness of this cover?

**10**

(*b*) Select at least **two** important examples of graphic design from different periods. Discuss the techniques used by the designers to achieve visual impact and originality.

**20**

**SECTION 2—DESIGN STUDIES (continued)**

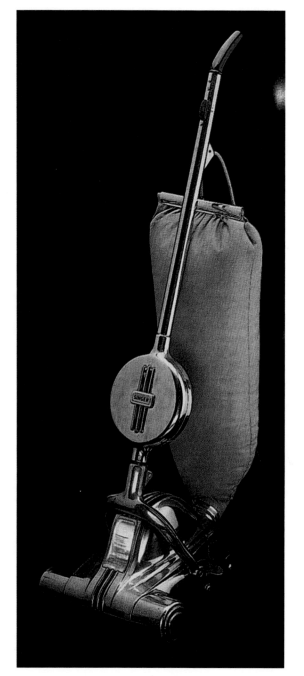

American vacuum cleaner by Malcolm Park (1938). Deluxe model with automatic cord rewind mechanism, aluminium case and cloth bag.

## 8. Product Design

*Marks*

(a) Comment on the style and use of materials involved in the design of this domestic appliance. Compare it with current designs for vacuum cleaners.

**10**

(b) Discuss the work of **two** product designers from different periods. Comment on the various ways in which they use styling and materials in order to create desirable and successful consumer goods.

**20**

**[Turn over**

**SECTION 2—DESIGN STUDIES (continued)**

Cafeteria in a trade fair complex in Leipzig designed by Frank Gehry (1995)

*Marks*

## 9. Interior Design

(*a*)   Comment on the way in which the designer of this cafeteria combines a variety of elements to create an overall effect. Do you think visitors would be attracted to this area? Give reasons for your answer.

**10**

(*b*)   Select **two** examples of interior design by designers from different periods. Describe these interiors and discuss the ideas, methods and materials used in order to make the concept a reality.

**20**

## SECTION 2—DESIGN STUDIES (continued)

Einstein Tower by Eric Mendelsohn (1921)

*Marks*

## 10. Environmental/Architectural Design

(*a*)  The Einstein Tower was designed in 1921 as an observatory and laboratory. Discuss the methods used by the architect to combine function with form. This style of architecture is known as "Expressionist". What do you think is meant by this, with reference to the Einstein Tower?    **10**

(*b*)  Select **two** examples of work by architects with highly contrasting styles. Explain how the architects have made use of form and materials to realise their concepts.    **20**

**[Turn over**

**SECTION 2—DESIGN STUDIES (continued)**

Ornamental Bodice Clasp by René Lalique (1898) gold, enamel, semi-precious stones and diamonds (wingspan 25cm)

*Marks*

## 11. Jewellery Design

(a) Discuss the way in which René Lalique uses materials in order to create striking and decorative effects in this piece of jewellery. Do you feel this is a wearable piece? Give reasons for your views. **10**

(b) By referring to at least **two** jewellery designers from different periods discuss how they use their sources of inspiration and materials to create unique and/or fashionable pieces. **20**

**SECTION 2—DESIGN STUDIES (continued)**

Summit Peak Jacket—3 layer Gore-tex R49 Fabric by SprayWay

*Marks*

## 12. Textile Design

(a) Analyse the important design features of this Spray Way jacket with particular reference to fabric, function and style. Why in your view are such jackets also fashionable?

**10**

(b) Sport is only one of many influences on the design of textiles. Select and describe **two** examples of textile or fashion design from different periods. Discuss the key factors which have influenced these designs.

**20**

*[END OF QUESTION PAPER]*

**Blank page**

2002 HIGHER

**X003/301**

NATIONAL
QUALIFICATIONS
2002

ART AND DESIGN

HIGHER

Paper 1

Practical Assignment

**The Practical Examinations for the 2002 examination diet may take place at the centre's discretion on the most convenient date in the period from Monday 29 April until Friday 10 May inclusive.**

**Time allowed: 3 hours**

50 marks are assigned to this paper.

Maximum sizes:     Two-dimensional work:  A2.
Three-dimensional work:  30 cm in greatest dimension.

Any medium except oil paint may be used.

SCOTTISH
QUALIFICATIONS
AUTHORITY

# GENERAL INSTRUCTIONS

Base your work for the Practical Assignment on your Expressive Activity unit **or** your Design Activity unit.

In the examination room you may refer to:

• Design **or** Expressive Folio of work

• Practical Assignment Form

You may use any three-dimensional source materials identified in the unit you have selected.

You will be allowed up to 20 minutes after the examination to assemble your work on the maximum number of sheets (2 × A2 sheets).

**This extension time is not to be used for producing examination work.**

Note: Mechanical reproductions of drawings and/or photographs from your folio by means such as TRACING, LIGHT BOXES and PHOTOCOPYING **will not be permitted during the examination**.

Select **either** SECTION A **or** SECTION B.

## SECTION A

### Expressive Activity

### Task

You should produce practical work which demonstrates your ability to develop and/or refine work carried out in your Expressive unit. This could take the form of new and further developments from your stimulus and might include extending ideas not fully explored within the work of your unit leading to alternative outcome(s).

**Remember that work produced for this Assignment should relate directly to your EXPRESSIVE unit theme and must develop, not simply copy, work already done. Further investigative work, such as analytical drawing, is not appropriate in this assignment.**

The following suggestions are provided to help you get started:

• produce work based on the stimulus or sources used by you but not fully explored in your Expressive unit

• produce work which emphasises a different style of approach to your chosen theme.

Work should be on a maximum of **two** A2 sheets or equivalent three-dimensional work. You may use any suitable media, materials or process.

## SECTION B

### Design Activity

### Task

You should produce practical work which demonstrates an alternative approach or approaches to work carried out in your Design unit. This could take the form of new and further developments from your brief and might include extending Design ideas not fully explored within the work of your unit.

**Remember that work produced for this Assignment should relate to your DESIGN brief and design unit and must develop, not simply copy, work already done. Further investigative work, such as analytical drawing, is not appropriate in this assignment.**

The following suggestions are provided to help you get started:

- develop design ideas which you considered but did not fully explore in your Design unit

- reconsider your solution and suggest further modifications and/or changes to improve it.

Work should be on a maximum of **two** A2 sheets or equivalent three-dimensional work. You may use any suitable media, materials or process.

*[END OF QUESTION PAPER]*

**Blank page**

# X003/302

| NATIONAL QUALIFICATIONS 2002 | FRIDAY, 7 JUNE 1.00PM – 3.00PM | ART AND DESIGN HIGHER Paper 2 |

There are **two** sections to this paper, Section 1—Art Studies; and Section 2—Design Studies. Each section is worth 40 marks.

Candidates should attempt questions as follows:

In SECTION 1 answer **ONE full question** (parts (*a*) and (*b*)) and **ONE part (*a*) only** of any other question

**and**

In SECTION 2 answer **ONE full question** (parts (*a*) and (*b*)) and **ONE part (*a*) only** of any other question.

You may use sketches to illustrate your answers.

SCOTTISH
QUALIFICATIONS
AUTHORITY

## SECTION 1—ART STUDIES

**Instructions**

Answer **ONE full question**, (parts (*a*) and (*b*)), and **ONE part (*a*) only** of any other question.

Ingres "Madame Moitessier" (1856) oil on canvas (120 × 92 cm)

*Marks*

## 1. Portraiture

(*a*) Discuss the ways in which Ingres portrays the status and personality of Madame Moitessier to us. In your answer, comment on pose, composition and use of visual elements. Explain your personal thoughts about the painting. **10**

(*b*) Compare examples of work by **two** artists from different movements or periods whose approaches to portraiture are contrasting. Comment on their working methods, styles and subjects. **20**

**SECTION 1—ART STUDIES (continued)**

George Segal "Bus Riders" (1964) plaster casts and bus seats (175·2 × 193 cm)

*Marks*

## 2. Figure Composition

*To create this sculpture, Segal made plaster casts of some of his friends.*

(a) Discuss the artist's method of creating sculpture. Comment on the use of form, texture and the scale of the sculpture. What thoughts and feelings does the sculpture communicate to you?

**10**

(b) Discuss examples of figure compositions by **two** artists from different movements or periods. Explain their working methods. Comment on how the artists have communicated their ideas about the compositional relationships between the figures in their work.

**20**

**[Turn over**

**SECTION 1—ART STUDIES (continued)**

Jack Knox "Summer Sundae" (1974) acrylic on canvas (121 × 116·8 cm)

*Marks*

## 3. Still Life

(a) Discuss the composition of this still life painting. Comment on the artist's use of colour, shape and line. What is your opinion of this approach to still life? **10**

(b) Discuss examples of still life by **two** artists from different movements or periods. To what extent are your chosen works typical of these artists? **20**

**SECTION 1—ART STUDIES (continued)**

Ferdinand Hodler "Lake Thun" (1905) oil on canvas (80·2 × 100 cm)

*Marks*

## 4. Natural Environment

(a) Discuss the subject and composition of this landscape painting. Comment on the artist's use of colour and shape. Explain what the painting makes you feel and think.

**10**

(b) Discuss examples of work by **two** artists from different movements or periods who have been inspired by the natural environment. Explain the methods used by them to create mood, atmosphere and a response to nature in their work.

**20**

**[Turn over**

**SECTION 1—ART STUDIES (continued)**

Richard Estes "Holland Hotel" (1984)  oil on canvas (114 × 181 cm)

*Marks*

## 5.   Built Environment

*This is a painting not a photograph.*

(*a*)   Discuss how you think the artist has created this highly realistic work.  Why do you think this scene appealed to Estes?  What is your opinion of the painting?     **10**

(*b*)   Select **two** artists from different movements or periods.  Discuss examples of their work which are inspired by the built environment.  Comment on their choice of subject, working methods and style.     **20**

**SECTION 1—ART STUDIES (continued)**

Calum Colvin "Mundus Subterraneus I" (*The Underworld*) (1996)
computer generated image (152 × 122 cm)

*Marks*

## 6. Fantasy and Imagination

*Colvin describes this piece as a large scale computer manipulated photographic artwork.*

(*a*) Discuss the content and composition of this work. Comment on the artist's methods in producing this imaginative piece. What is your personal interpretation of the image?

**10**

(*b*) Work based on fantasy and imagination is often difficult to fully understand. Discuss your interpretation of examples of this theme by **two** artists from different movements or periods. Explain the methods used by the artists to communicate their ideas.

**20**

## SECTION 2—DESIGN STUDIES

**Instructions**

Answer **ONE full question**, (parts (*a*) and (*b*)), and **ONE part (*a*) only** of any other question.

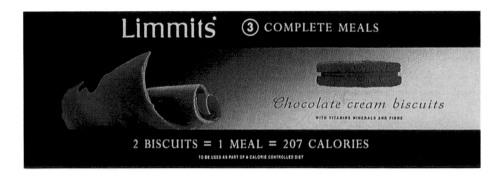

Design by Lewis Moberley (Design Team), Art Director Mary Lewis. This image shows a range of designs for biscuit products.

*Marks*

## 7. Graphic Design

(*a*) Discuss the ways in which colour, photography and layout have been used to create a strong marketing image for the packaging of slimming products. How effective is this in your opinion? **10**

(*b*) Graphic designers always seek to communicate powerfully with their audiences. Select at least **two** graphic designers or design groups working in different periods or styles and compare their work. Focus in particular on those aspects of their designs which make them effective. **20**

## SECTION 2—DESIGN STUDIES (continued)

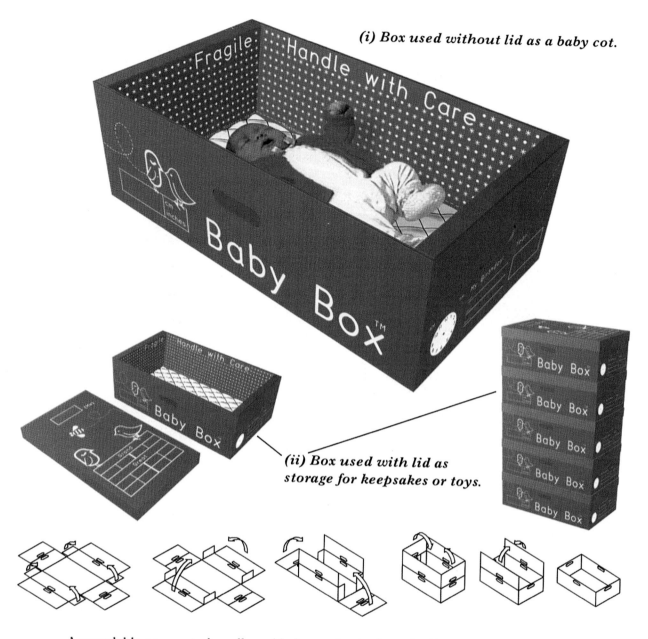

*(i) Box used without lid as a baby cot.*

*(ii) Box used with lid as storage for keepsakes or toys.*

A recyclable corrugated cardboard baby cot by Andrew Stafford, 2001

*Marks*

## 8. Product Design

(a) What do you think the designer considered were important issues when he developed his ideas for this product? In your opinion how successful has he been and why?

**10**

(b) Select **two** designers or groups of designers working in different periods or styles. With reference to particular designs, discuss some of their most important ideas and approaches to the designing of products.

**20**

**[Turn over**

## SECTION 2—DESIGN STUDIES (continued)

Foyer of the Granada Cinema, Tooting, London 1931.
Interior Designer, Theodore Komisarjevsky

*Marks*

## 9. Interior Design

(*a*) In which ways does the designer's approach to the interior design of a cinema foyer differ from current cinema design? In your opinion which issues should be considered in the designing of such spaces? **10**

(*b*) Compare the work of **two** interior designers from different periods or working in different styles. What in your view are their main priorities as interior designers? **20**

**SECTION 2—DESIGN STUDIES (continued)**

Casa Batlló apartment block façade, Barcelona (1904–1907). Polished and carved stone and metalwork. Architect, Antoni Gaudi.

*Marks*

## 10. Environmental/Architectural Design

(a) Evaluate the way in which Gaudi combines form, function and aesthetic appeal in this design for a block of flats in an inner city setting. Compare this block of flats in terms of its visual impact to any blocks known to you. Which do you prefer and why?

**10**

(b) Select **two** architects working in different periods or styles. Discuss the key features, function and aesthetic qualities of their work. You should make reference to particular buildings in your answer.

**20**

**[Turn over**

**SECTION 2—DESIGN STUDIES (continued)**

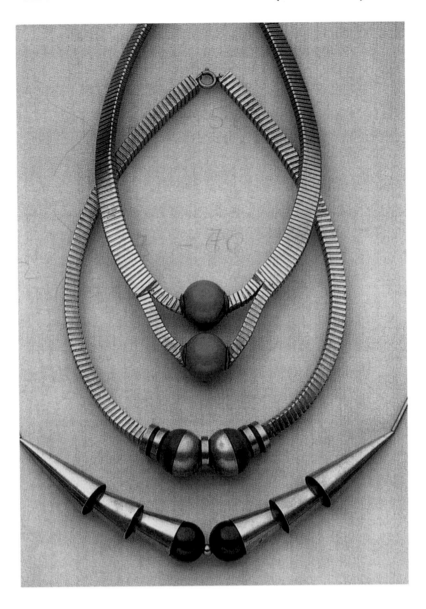

Necklaces in chrome and bakelite plastic, unknown French designer, mid 1920s

*Marks*

## 11. Jewellery Design

(a) In your opinion what are the most striking features of these necklaces? Discuss the ways in which the designer has used materials and forms. What sources of inspiration might have been used for these pieces?    **10**

(b) Evaluate the work of **two** jewellers from different periods or working in different styles. Show in your answer how they use materials, visual stimuli or other sources to create interesting and stylish pieces.    **20**

**SECTION 2—DESIGN STUDIES (continued)**

Japanese street-style fashion, mid 1990s

*Marks*

## 12. Textile Design

(a) Discuss this example of recent Japanese youth street style. Compare this with other examples of popular street fashion for young people. In your opinion why do such styles appeal to this age group?

**10**

(b) Fashion and textiles are design areas particularly subject to change and innovation. Discuss the work of **two** textile or fashion designers working in different periods or styles. What important changes did they contribute to fashion and/or textile design?

**20**

*[END OF QUESTION PAPER]*

**Blank page**

# X003/301

NATIONAL
QUALIFICATIONS
2003

ART AND DESIGN

HIGHER

Paper 1

Practical Assignment

**The Practical Examinations for the 2003 examination diet may take place at the centre's discretion on the most convenient date in the period from Monday 28 April until Friday 9 May inclusive.**

**Time allowed:  3 hours**

50 marks are assigned to this paper.

Maximum sizes:     Two-dimensional work:  A2.
Three-dimensional work:  30 cm in greatest dimension.

Any medium except oil paint may be used.

SCOTTISH
QUALIFICATIONS
AUTHORITY

## GENERAL INSTRUCTIONS

Base your work for the Practical Assignment on your Expressive Activity folio **or** your Design Activity folio.

In the examination room you may refer to:

- Design **or** Expressive Folio of work
- Practical Assignment Form

You may use any three-dimensional source materials identified in the folio you have selected.

You will be allowed up to 20 minutes after the examination to assemble your work on the maximum number of sheets (2 × A2 sheets).

**This extension time is not to be used for producing examination work.**

Note: Mechanical reproductions of drawings and/or photographs copied from your folio by means such as TRACING, LIGHT BOXES and PHOTOCOPYING **will not be permitted during the examination.** This exclusion also includes images and/or information copied from folios and stored on disk, CD or digital camera.

Select **either** SECTION A **or** SECTION B.

### SECTION A

**Expressive Activity**

**Task**

You should produce practical work which demonstrates your ability to develop and/or refine work carried out in your Expressive folio. This could take the form of new and further developments from your stimulus and might include extending ideas leading to alternative outcome(s) not fully explored within the work of your folio.

**Remember that work produced for this Assignment should relate directly to your EXPRESSIVE folio theme and must develop, not copy, work already done. Further investigative work, such as analytical drawing, is not appropriate in this Assignment.**

The following suggestions are provided to help you get started:

- produce work based on the stimulus or sources used by you but not fully explored in the work of your Expressive folio
- produce work which emphasises a different style of approach to your chosen theme.

Work should be on a maximum of **two** A2 sheets or equivalent three-dimensional work. You may use any suitable media, materials or process.

**SECTION B**

**Design Activity**

**Task**

You should produce practical work which demonstrates an alternative approach or approaches to work carried out in your Design folio. This could take the form of new and further developments from your brief and might include extending Design ideas not fully explored within the work of your folio.

**Remember that work produced for this Assignment should relate to your DESIGN brief and design folio and must develop, not copy, work already done. Further investigative work, such as analytical drawing, is not appropriate in this Assignment.**

The following suggestions are provided to help you get started:

- develop design ideas which you considered but did not fully explore in the work of your Design folio

- reconsider your solution and suggest further modifications and/or changes to improve it.

Work should be on a maximum of **two** A2 sheets or equivalent three-dimensional work. You may use any suitable media, materials or process.

*[END OF QUESTION PAPER]*

*Page three*

[BLANK PAGE]

# X003/302

| NATIONAL QUALIFICATIONS 2003 | THURSDAY, 5 JUNE 1.00 PM – 3.00 PM | ART AND DESIGN HIGHER Paper 2 |

There are **two** sections to this paper, Section 1—Art Studies; and Section 2—Design Studies. Each section is worth 40 marks.

Candidates should attempt questions as follows:

In SECTION 1 answer **ONE full question** (parts *(a)* and *(b)*) and **ONE part (*a*) only** of any other question

**and**

In SECTION 2 answer **ONE full question** (parts *(a)* and *(b)*) and **ONE part (*a*) only** of any other question.

You may use sketches to illustrate your answers.

SCOTTISH
QUALIFICATIONS
AUTHORITY

## SECTION 1—ART STUDIES

**Instructions**

Answer **ONE full question** (parts (*a*) and (*b*)), and **ONE part (*a*) only** of any other question.

John Everett Millais   *The Bridesmaid* (1851) oil on panel (27·9 × 20·3 cm)

## 1.   Portraiture

*Marks*

(*a*)   Discuss the composition of this portrait.   Comment on the use of visual elements and media handling.   In your opinion, how successfully has the artist communicated his thoughts about the bridesmaid?   **10**

(*b*)   Discuss examples of portraiture by **two** artists from different movements or periods.   Comment on their choice of subjects and working methods.   To what extent has their work influenced other artists?   **20**

**SECTION 1—ART STUDIES (continued)**

Joyce Cairns   *Last Supper* (1989) oil on board (205·8 × 235·2 cm)

## 2.   **Figure Composition**

*Marks*

(*a*)   Discuss the composition of this painting.   Comment on **at least two** of the following:

*colour;   line;   distortion;   perspective.*

In what way does the title affect your interpretation of this work?   **10**

(*b*)   Discuss examples of figure composition by **two** artists from different movements or periods.   Comment on the differences and/or similarities in their approaches and working methods.   Explain why you consider them to be important artists.   **20**

**[Turn over**

**SECTION 1—ART STUDIES (continued)**

Meret Oppenheim   *Object: Breakfast in Fur* (1936) cup, saucer and spoon covered with fur

*Marks*

## 3.   Still Life

(*a*)   Discuss the choice of materials and method used by the artist to create this still life.  How do you think it challenges traditional approaches to still life? What is your personal opinion of the piece?                                               **10**

(*b*)   Compare examples of still life by **two** artists from different movements or periods.  Discuss the artists' particular contribution to still life and comment on their choice of subject matter, styles and working methods.                        **20**

**SECTION 1—ART STUDIES (continued)**

J.M.W. Turner   *Norham Castle, Sunrise* (1840–45) oil on canvas (90·8 × 121·9 cm)
© Tate, London 2003

## 4.   Natural Environment                                                              *Marks*

(*a*)   Discuss the methods used by Turner to produce this response to nature.   In
doing so, comment on his use of colour, shape and media handling.   How
successful do you think Turner has been in capturing the atmosphere of a
particular moment?                                                                          **10**

(*b*)   Discuss examples of work by **two** artists from different movements or periods
who have been inspired by the natural environment.   What similarities exist in
their work and in which ways do they differ?   Explain why you consider them
to be important artists.                                                                    **20**

**[Turn over**

**SECTION 1—ART STUDIES (continued)**

L.S. Lowry    *A Manufacturing Town* (1922) oil on board (43·2 × 53·3 cm)

## 5.  **Built Environment**

*Marks*

(*a*)  How successful do you think Lowry has been in communicating the industrial nature of this town to the viewer?  In your response comment on **at least two** of the following:

   *colour;    tone;    shape;    perspective.*

**10**

(*b*)  Discuss examples of work, within this theme, by **two** artists from different movements or periods.  Comment on their choice of subject matter and treatment of it.  Explain why you consider these artists to be influential.

**20**

**SECTION 1—ART STUDIES (continued)**

Marc Chagall   *I and the Village* (1911) oil on canvas (192·1 × 151·4 cm)

## 6.  Fantasy and Imagination

*Marks*

(*a*)  This painting is based on the artist's memories of childhood.  Discuss the methods used by the artist to create this image which conveys his personal experience.  Briefly give your opinion of the painting.

**10**

(*b*)  Select **two** artists from different movements or periods whose work is based on fantasy and imagination.  Discuss examples of their work and explain the methods used to communicate their ideas.  Why do you consider the artists you have selected to be important contributors to this theme?

**20**

**[Turn over**

## SECTION 2—DESIGN STUDIES

**Instructions**

Answer **ONE full question** (parts (*a*) and (*b*)), and **ONE part (*a*) only** of any other question.

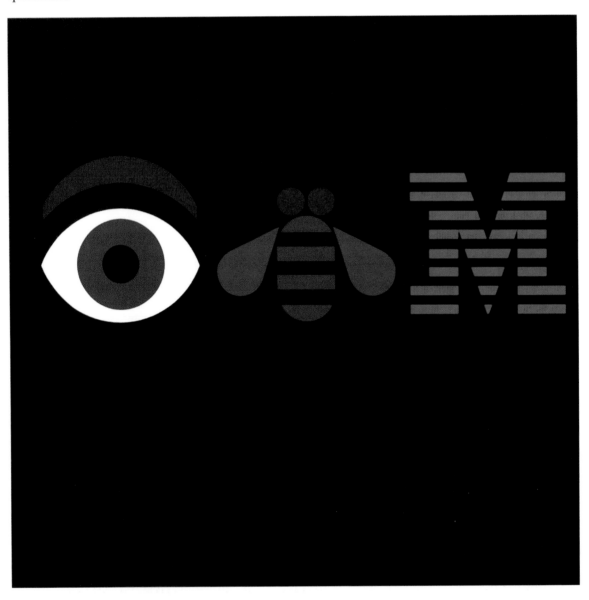

Poster design for International Business Machines (IBM), by Paul Rand (1981)

*Marks*

## 7. Graphic Design

(*a*)  Identify the key design features of this poster.  What message does it communicate, and how well does it succeed?  Justify your answer.  **10**

(*b*)  Select **two** designers from different periods or working in different styles. Discuss examples of their graphic designs that incorporate text and/or imagery in the layout.  How has the work of these designers contributed to the communication of marketing ideas and/or corporate identity?  **20**

## SECTION 2—DESIGN STUDIES (continued)

*Detail of camera lens.*

Mobile phone with Multimedia Messaging Service (MMS) and built-in camera.
Model 7250 by Nokia (2003).

*Marks*

## 8. Product Design

(*a*) Discuss the strengths and weaknesses of this multi-functional communication tool. In your response refer to **at least two** of the following:

*style; function; safety and security; technology; materials;*

*cultural trends.* **10**

(*b*) Select **two** product designers working in different periods or styles. Comment on the ways that their designs have improved the quality of everyday life. Refer to specific examples in your answer. **20**

**[Turn over**

**SECTION 2—DESIGN STUDIES (continued)**

Chiat Day Offices, New York City, designed by Gaetano Pesce (1993–96)

## 9. Interior Design

*Marks*

(a) How does this interior differ from a typical office environment? Which key design elements contribute to its effectiveness as a workspace? Do you think the designer has created a successful solution? Justify your answer. **10**

(b) Compare **two** interior designers from different periods or who work in contrasting styles. Highlight the main features of their work and state why they are considered to be important designers. **20**

## SECTION 2—DESIGN STUDIES (continued)

*Main entrance, Renfrew Street.*

*North facing facade.*

Glasgow School of Art, designed by Charles Rennie Mackintosh (1897/1909)

## 10. Environmental/Architectural Design

*Marks*

(a) What are the key features of this architectural design that contribute to its distinctive appearance? Identify what you think the architect's primary design considerations would have been in relation to the function of this building. Give reasons in support of your answer.

**10**

(b) Select **two** architects or environmental designers from different periods or who work in highly contrasting styles. Discuss the characteristics of their work and show, with reference to materials, form and innovation, why they are important figures in this area of design.

**20**

**[Turn over**

**SECTION 2—DESIGN STUDIES (continued)**

Two examples of Brooches of Coloured Tears designed by Wendy Ramshaw (1998).
Each brooch is 27 cm × 7 cm and made of 18ct gold with multi-coloured stones.

## 11. Jewellery Design

*Marks*

(a) How well does Wendy Ramshaw's design capture the theme? Refer to her use of materials, colour, shape and form in your answer. In what circumstances might this jewellery be worn? Give reasons.

**10**

(b) "Influences and visual stimuli are highly important factors in the development of exciting jewellery ideas." Select **two** jewellery designers, who work in different periods or styles, and discuss this statement in relation to their work. Why are they regarded as important designers?

**20**

**SECTION 2—DESIGN STUDIES (continued)**

Evening Coat with Embroidery designed by Elsa Schiaparelli (1937)

## 12. Textile Design

*Marks*

(a) What important design issues were considered in the development of this fashion item? In your response refer to **at least two** of the following:

*colour; texture; ambiguity; materials; form; humour.*

What is your opinion of this coat? **10**

(b) Fashion and textile designers are required to produce ideas for different target markets. Select **two** fashion/textile designers working in different periods or styles. Show, with reference to examples of their work, how they have responded to this challenge. Why are they important designers? **20**

*[END OF QUESTION PAPER]*

**[BLANK PAGE]**

**[BLANK PAGE]**

# Acknowledgements

| Question | Name of picture & artist | © Holder | Provider of transparency / file |
|---|---|---|---|
| 2000 P2 Q1 | *The Heroic Dosser* Peter Howson* | Angela Flowers Gallery | Angela Flowers |
| 2000 P2 Q2 | *The Rehearsal* Edgar Degas | © Glasgow Museums: Burrell Collection | ----- |
| 2000 P2 Q3 | *Glasses, Newspaper and a bottle of Wine* Gris | © Bridgeman Art Gallery | Bridgeman |
| 2000 P2 Q5 | *The Constructors* Fernand Leger | © Bridgeman Art Gallery | ADAG, Paris and DACS, London 2003 |
| 2000 P2 Q7 | *Dig For Victory* poster* | Photograph courtesy of Imperial War Museum, London | |
| 2000 P2 Q8 | *Juicy Salif* Philippe Starck* | Alessi SPA | Alessi SPA |
| 2000 P2 Q12 | *Conceptual Chic* Zandra Rhodes | Zandra Rhodes | ----- |
| 2001 P2 Q1 | *Goggle Head* Elizabeth Frink* | © Beaux Arts | Beaux Arts |
| 2001 P2 Q3 | *The Vegetable Stall* W. Y. MacGregor | © National Gallery of Scotland | ----- |
| 2001 P2 Q4 | *Fruit Fields* Duncan Shanks* | Duncan Shanks | ----- |
| 2001 P2 Q5 | *Pharmacy* Damien Hirst* | Damien Hirst | ----- |
| 2001 P2 Q10 | *Einstein* Tower Eric Mendelsohn | © AKG | ----- |
| 2001 P2 Q11 | *Bodice Clasp* Rene Lalique | © ADAGP, Paris and DACS, London 2003 | ----- |
| 2001 P2 Q12 | *Summit Peak Jacket* | Sprayway | Sprayway |
| 2002 P2 Q1 | *Madame Moitessier* Ingres | The National Gallery | The National Gallery |
| 2002 P2 Q3 | *Summer Sundae* Jack Knox* | Jack Knox | Jack Knox |
| 2002 P2 Q4 | *Lake Thun* Ferdinand Hodler* | Musee d'Art et d'Histoire Ville de Geneve | Musee d'Art at d'Histoire |
| 2002 P2 Q5 | *Holland Hotel* Richard Estes | © Richard Estes, Marlborough Gallery New York | ----- |
| 2002 P2 Q6 | *Mundus Subterraneus* Calum Colvin* | Calum Colvin | ----- |
| 2002 P2 Q9 | *Granada Cinema* Theodore Komisarjevsky | ©Arcaid Photography Agency | ----- |
| 2002 P2 Q10 | *Casa Batlló* Antoni Gaudi | ©Arcaid Photography Agency | ----- |
| 2003 P2 Q1 | *The Bridesmaid* John Everett Millais | Fitzwilliam Museum, Cambridge | Fitzwilliam Museum |
| 2003 P2 Q2 | *The Last Supper in Footdee* Joyce Cairns* | Joyce Cairns | Joyce Cairns |
| 2003 P2 Q3 | *Breakfast in Fur* Meret Oppenheim | © Photo SCALA, Florence | ----- |
| 2003 P2 Q4 | *Norham Castle Sunrise* J.M.W. Turner | © Tate London 2003 | Tate London 2003 |
| 2003 P2 Q6 | *I and the Village* Marc Chagall | © Photo SCALA, Florence | ----- |
| 2003 P2 Q8 | *Nokia Mobile Phone* | © Nokia | ----- |
| 2003 P2 Q10 | *GSA Photos* Taschen Köln* | © Anthony Oliver | ----- |
| 2003 P2 Q11 | *Brooches of Coloured Tears* Wendy Ramshaw* | © Bob Camp | ----- |

2000 P2 Q6 *Autumnal Cannibalism* Salvador Dali: © Salvador Dali, Gala Salvador Dali Foundation, DACS, London 2003, © Tate, London 2003
2001 P2 Q6 *Sleeping Gypsy* Henri Rousseau: © Photo SCALA, Florence, © 2003 The Museum of Modern Art / Scala, Florence
2001 P2 Q7   Photo by Peter Robathon (Katz/Outline) From *Rolling Stone* August 21 1997, © Rolling Stone LLC. All rights reserved. Reprint by permission*
2002 P2 Q2 *Bus Riders* George Segal: Hirshhorn Museum and Sculpture Garden, Smithsonian Institution, Gift of Joseph H. Hirshhorn, 1966.
2003 P2 Q7 *IBM Poster* Paul Rand: Reprinted with permission © 1981 by International Business Machines Corporation.*

* indicates that the copyright holder has generously permitted the reproduction of the item free of charge.